Do

Kaye Umansky w̲   ̲m̲o̲u̲t̲h̲, Devon. Her favourite
books as a child were the *Just William* books, *Alice's
Adventures in Wonderland*, *The Hobbit* and *The Swish of the
Curtain*. She went to teachers' training college, and then she
taught in London primary schools for twelve years, specializ-
ing in music and drama. In her spare time she sang and played
keyboards with a semi-professional soul band.

She now writes full time – or as full time as she can in
between trips to Sainsbury's and looking after her husband
(Mo), daughter (Ella, aged ten) and cats (Charlie and Alfie).

Kaye Umansky

Do Not Open Before
Christmas Day!

Illustrated by Garry Davies

PUFFIN BOOKS

PUFFIN BOOKS

Published by the Penguin Group
Penguin Books Ltd, 27 Wrights Lane, London W8 5TZ, England
Penguin Putnam Inc., 375 Hudson Street, New York, New York 10014, USA
Penguin Books Australia Ltd, Ringwood, Victoria, Australia
Penguin Books Canada Ltd, 10 Alcorn Avenue, Toronto, Ontario, Canada M4V 3B2
Penguin Books (NZ) Ltd, Private Bag 102902, NSMC, Auckland New Zealand

Penguin Books Ltd, Registered Offices: Harmondsworth, Middlesex, England

Published in Puffin Books 1993
5 7 9 10 8 6 4

Text copyright © Kaye Umansky, 1993
Illustrations copyright © Garry Davies, 1993
All rights reserved

The moral right of the author has been asserted

Typeset by Datix International Limited, Bungay, Suffolk
Printed in England by Clays Ltd, St Ives plc

Except in the United States of America, this book is sold subject to the condition
that it shall not, by way of trade or otherwise, be lent, re-sold, hired out, or otherwise
circulated without the publisher's prior consent in any form of binding or cover
other than that in which it is published and without a similar condition including this
condition being imposed on the subsequent purchaser.

British Library Cataloguing in Publication Data
A CIP catalogue record for this book is available from the British Library

ISBN 0–140–36630X

All I Want for Christmas is . . .

Tarzan: *Overcoming Your Fear of Heights* by Lee Poff; a big bottle of Jungle Man (perfume, not cologne); a new loincloth (size large, £9.99. They do them in Marks).

King Kong: A very, very, very big banana. And don't bother to gift wrap it, I'll eat it straight away. I love bananas. Please send me all your unwanted bananas. You could call this a banana appeal.

The India Rubber Man: A Christmas cake with a file in it, because I'm going to jail for a long stretch.

The Lone Ranger: Another pistol. I need two, in case one won't shoot far enough.

Humpty-Dumpty: Well, I always think a hard-boiled egg is hard to beat. How long do I like it? Oh, about two and a half inches . . .

Mary Poppins: A new umbrella. My old one's seen better days. I guess you could say it's had its ups and downs.

Dr Who: I'm not sure. My heart says a new Tardis, my mind says some new underpants, and I haven't heard from my liver yet.

The Old Woman who Lived in the Shoe: A book on how to raise children. Yesterday, I threw them all down a manhole.

The Thin Man: Some razor-blades. I want to sharpen my appetite.

Jaws: I think I'm going deaf. I could do with a herring-aid.

Christmas Day in the Wicked Queen's Palace

WICKED QUEEN: Oh, Gerald, look! Look at this sweet card! It's from Snow White and Prince Leopold! Isn't that kind? You see, I *told* you she'd come round. It's got a dear little robin on it, look. I wonder if it's one of the little woodland creatures that helped her when she got lost in the forest that time? Recycled paper by the look of it. Terribly poor quality. Oh, and look! Here's one from the seven dwarfs! 'Lousy Christmas and a rotten new year, from Grumpy and the boys.' Charming. Oh, wait a minute, there's something else. 'Hope you like the present we bought you. Snow White and Leopold chipped in.' What present?

KING: Over there, darling. Delivered this
         morning.

WICKED QUEEN: [*Tearing off paper*] Oh,
         look, Gerald, it's another magic
         mirror! How thoughtful. Let's hope it's
         better quality than the last one. I'll just
         see if it's working properly.

KING: Must you do it now, darling? I was
         rather hoping for breakfast.

WICKED QUEEN: Shush.
         'Mirror, mirror on the wall,
         Who is the fairest of them all?'

MIRROR: You're asking me who is most fair?
          Not you, ferret-face. So there!

WICKED QUEEN: [*Smashing it*] I suppose
          they think that's funny. Gerald, send
          for the huntsman. I say, I'm having a
          smashing time.

KING: It's Christmas, darling. He's got the
          day off. Let's have the turkey and
          forget all about it, eh?

WICKED QUEEN: Oh, very well. Here's
          my gift to you, darling.

KING: Oh, some lovely hankies. How
          thoughtful, darling. Here's mine to
          you.

WICKED QUEEN: Oh, darling! A whole
          new set of fatal poisons! And gift-
          wrapped too. What a super surprise.
          I can't wait to try them out. You know,
          darling, I've been thinking. Perhaps
          we should let bygones be bygones.
          You're right. Who needs all this ill
          feeling? Let's start the New Year with
          a little party. Just close family, you
          know, and a few good friends. Snow
          White, perhaps, and Leopold, and
          maybe the dwarfs. What do you
          think . . .?

Something Easy to do After your Christmas Dinner!

Across:
3. STOCKING
4. PANTOMIME
7. RED
9. DONKEY
10. ELF
12. CAROL
13. GEESE

ACROSS

3 It's hung up about Christmas (8)
4 Christmas show (9)
7 Rudolph's nose was this (3)
9 Mary rode on one (6)
10 Santa's 'Little Helper' was one (3)
12 This girl sings Christmas music (5)
13 Christmas is coming, the _____ is getting fat (5)

DOWN

1 Santa's laugh (4)
2 Gabriel was one (5)
4 A traditional Christmas dessert (7)
5 You gobble these down (7)
6 Joseph's wife (4)
8 They pull the sleigh (4)
11 Snow does this (5)

Answers on page 127

Silly Carols

Jingle Bells

Jingle bells, conker shells
Make a lovely meal.
Uncle Warren
Lost his sporran
In the Scottish reel.

While Shepherds Munched

While shepherds munched their chocs by
    night
All seated by a stream,
The Monster of the Deep rose up
And pinched the coffee cream.

'Oi! Give us back our coffee cream,'
The angry shepherds said.
The Monster merely smiled, and took
The marzipan instead.

OR

While shepherds lie on rocks all night
And backache comes to pass,
The sheep are not so stupid
And prefer to lie on grass.

We Three Kings

We three kings of Orient are,
One on the drums and one on guitar,
One on the bass, who's feeding his face
With a Twix and a Yorkie Bar.

Oh-oh
What a racket, what a noise.
Those three kings are noisy boys.
Pay them quick, before they're sick,
And send them back to Illinois.

Good King Wenceslas

Good King Wenceslas looked out,
Saw that it was raining,
Couldn't find his welly boot,
Spent an hour complaining.
'Someone here has nicked my boot.
I can't find my welly.
Never mind, I'll stay indoors
And see what's on the telly.'

A Letter from Rudolph

30 The Pines
Lapland

Christmas Day

Deer Mum

I expect you were a bit surprised to find me
not in bed this morning. I left a note on the
kitchen table, but of course Ralph and Roland
and Robert and the others will have torn it up.
That's just the sort of mean thing they would
do. You know how they always gang up and
laugh at me and call me names and won't let
me join in their reindeer games just because
I'm more intelligent than them. Anyway, here's
what happened:

Last night, Christmas Eve that is, they turned
me out of the bedroom again, saying I was a
swot and they couldn't sleep because of my
nose. You know, the usual sort of thing. That's
after they tried putting sticking-plaster over it
and rubbing boot polish on it and sticking
signs on my head saying 'Danger – Fire Risk',
and loads of other mean things. I almost came
to tell you, but I heard you were watching
Bambi again, and I didn't think you'd want me
to interrupt.

Anyway, I went to sleep in the spare room.
Did you know about the spring sticking up in

the spare bed? It meant I couldn't get to sleep, so I sat up reading the dictionary, which is just as well because suddenly I heard the sound of jingling bells and lots of small hooves trampling about on the roof. Something was coming down the chimney as well! Heart pounding, I sat up, just as this tubby figure all in red comes sliding out with a *whoosh*!

Yes, it was Santa! He came and plonked himself down on the end of my bed. Got some nasty sooty marks on the bedspread, but I didn't like to say anything.

'Rudolph,' he says to me. 'I've heard about you. You have a very shiny nose, do you not?'

I could have died of shame.

'Yes,' I whispered in a low voice, 'I do have a somewhat ruddy olfactory organ. You might even say it glows.'

'I thought so. Well, it's foggy out there, and without wasting any more time, I'm going to ask a favour. Rudolph, with your nose so bright, won't you guide my sleigh tonight? How about it?'

'Santa,' I said. 'I'm your ruminant quadruped of family Cervidae with deciduous branching horns [deer]. Look no further.'

And that's exactly what happened. I was hitched to the front of the team, Santa sprinkled me with Flying Dust, and off we flew. The rest of the night passed in a magical blur, and before I knew it, the last present was given away and the sun was beginning to rise.

'Rudolph,' said Santa. 'Come back with me

and have a wonderful Christmas dinner, and take your pick of any presents you like as your reward for your tireless work on behalf of others.'

'I will,' I said. 'But first let me put the sleigh away.'

And guess what I found lying in the bottom? Presents for Ralph, Roland and Robert! Isn't that an amazing coincidence? That they were the only presents that, by some tragic accident, didn't get delivered?

I do hope they weren't too disappointed.

Anyway, I shall be back in a day or two. Have a lovely Christmas.

Your son
Rudolph

Applications for Rudolph's Job

VACANCY
Sleigh Team Leader

(£5 for the night and as much hay as you can eat)

Owing to Rudolph's sudden indisposition (a nasty case of deer ear), Santa finds himself in urgent need of a replacement sleigh leader.

The successful applicant will be preferably four legged and must have a good head for heights. Preference will be given to applicants with red noses.

Please send a colour photo of your nose with application. BOX 546.

NAME: Dobbin the horse

PERSONAL DETAILS: I know I am not a reindeer, but I think I would make a great team-leader because I possess the five H's. Four Hooves, a Head for Heights, and a Happy smile. And don't tell me that's more than five. Where does it say a team-leader has to count? And if people say, 'Who's that thundering great horse pulling Santa's sleigh?' I shall cough politely and reply, 'Excuse me, I'm a little horse,' thus getting myself a reputation as a bit of a joker. I do not, of course, have a red nose. But then, who does?

NAME: Coco the Clown

PERSONAL DETAILS: Me. I do. I also have a good head for heights and a degree in Advanced Trampolining. I do not have four legs, but to discount me on these grounds would be pure legism. And don't forget, I can keep up the reindeer's morale by telling jokes and squirting them in the eye with water from the hysterically funny fake flower I wear on my lapel.

NAME: Muffin the Mule

PERSONAL DETAILS: I'd be a great team-
leader. I'd be really stubborn, right,
cos that's what we mules are best at. I
could really dig my heels in and cause
pile-ups on the roofs, har, har, an'
give those bloomin' snooty reindeer
something to think about, anyway.
Wadya mean that's not the spirit? Look,
there's no point tryin' ter persuade
me I'm not team material because I've
made up my mind I'm 'aving this job,
right? And no, I don't 'ave a red nose
and I don't care about that neither.

NAME: Horace the husky

PERSONAL DETAILS: I'm ideal. Four legs, good at pulling, and used to nasty weather conditions. And if people say to me, 'What's a dirty great husky like you doing pulling Santa's sleigh?' I shall give a little cough and say, 'Excuse me, I'm a little husky.' That'll make them laugh, I bet. A lot more than they'll laugh at Dobbin the horse, anyway. I'll probably end up more popular than Rudolph, red nose or no red nose.

NAME: A sheep

PERSONAL DETAILS: People think we sheep are all the same, don't they, Stan? They think all we do is follow each other around going baa, and that we never have a single thought of our own. Isn't that right, Sheila? Utter nonsense of course, isn't it, Dirk? I think I'd make a very good team-leader, wouldn't I, everyone? All together now, let's follow Noreen, baa . . .

Reindeer Poems

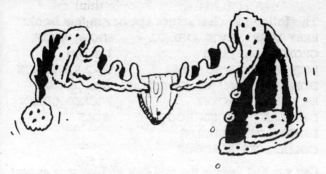

The Reindeer's Lament

On Christmas eve, a reindeer
Is an animal of note.
But from January onwards,
Just a place to hang your coat.

Limerick

An ambitious young reindeer called Ray
Applied to be Head of the Sleigh.
When asked, 'Does it glow?'
He had to say, 'No.'
And was instantly told, 'Go away.'

Wordsearch

The following characters appear in this book:

BABY BEAR	JACK AND JILL	SNOW WHITE
CINDERELLA	JAWS	TARZAN
DICK TOCK	KING KONG	UNCLE WARREN
DOBBIN	MAJOR SPOILSPORT	WENCESLAS
DR WHO	PORKY	WICKED QUEEN
DRUSILLA	ROBIN HOOD	WOLF
ESMERELDA	RUDOLPH	
GOLDILOCKS	SCROOGE	

Can you find them in the grid below? They may appear
up, down, diagonally, backwards, or forwards.

```
S  B  A  B  Y  B  E  A  R  M  O  N  A  Z  R  A  T  W  L  H
K  C  V  Y  W  A  H  P  E  J  S  Z  V  N  P  Q  A  I  T  E
C  G  R  I  Y  G  F  T  V  N  K  L  L  O  I  P  H  C  G  S
O  O  O  O  X  Z  F  L  D  O  B  B  I  N  U  D  S  K  G  D
L  K  B  S  O  G  H  J  O  P  L  B  I  G  A  M  O  E  G  R
I  L  I  G  T  G  C  D  V  E  K  C  O  T  K  C  I  D  H  W
D  N  N  P  R  Y  E  T  R  I  W  I  D  D  O  N  T  Q  J  H
L  A  H  B  O  C  E  U  B  U  S  I  N  N  V  D  Y  U  N  O
O  R  O  M  P  E  D  E  R  S  S  L  P  G  T  R  X  E  B  E
G  I  O  L  S  O  L  T  N  R  W  I  J  V  K  R  E  E  N  T
L  O  D  X  L  U  T  E  E  R  S  P  L  C  B  O  T  N  U  J
G  L  A  P  I  G  Y  K  R  O  P  T  O  L  X  C  N  F  A  M
C  H  H  R  O  F  A  R  R  T  O  L  K  V  A  P  H  G  R  A
S  T  E  F  P  J  K  X  A  L  L  E  R  E  D  N  I  C  Y  M
R  T  W  G  S  Q  U  E  W  E  N  C  E  S  L  A  S  T  F  W
A  D  L  E  R  E  M  S  E  T  R  E  E  D  A  Z  P  L  O  O
O  P  I  T  O  E  N  D  L  I  T  R  E  W  S  H  O  P  I  P
P  S  W  A  J  G  B  V  C  P  L  E  T  I  H  W  W  O  N  S
A  D  S  G  A  I  Y  H  N  D  U  K  U  Y  O  P  H  R  Y  D
M  N  O  A  M  P  I  B  U  J  A  C  K  A  N  D  J  I  L  L
```

Answers on page 128

Celebrity Interview with Sid 'No Room' Barraclough, Innkeeper

Interviewer: Are you aware that you have gone down in history as a complete bozo? That you are the part nobody wants in the school play? And all because of those two little words.

Sid: *Well, it's easy to say that now, innit? I mean, if you ain't got a room, you ain't got a room, and that's all there is to it. How was I supposed to know who they was anyway? I didn't know they was that important. I was rushed off me feet at the time. There's only me and the missis.*

Interviewer: And the fact that a heaving great star had removed itself from its accustomed place in the sky and was hanging directly above their heads didn't tell you anything?

Sid: *There's low beams in my inn. I'm used to seein' stars.*

Interviewer:	So you're saying that two of the most important people in history turn up at your inn and you couldn't offer them a bed?
Sid:	*Oh yes, I had a bed. It wasn't the bed that was the trouble. I just didn't have a room to put it in.*
Interviewer:	Not even a shed or something?
Sid:	*Yeah, I gotta shed. But it's got stuff in it. The mower an' that. The coal. The deck-chairs. It's small.*
Interviewer:	Fred Stanwyk up the road managed to find them a place, though, didn't he?
Sid:	*Fred Stanwyk's got a stable. I keep pointin' it out, but no one ever listens. I don't 'ave a stable. All I've got is a very small shed.*
Interviewer:	Are you upset at Fred Stanwyk winning the coveted Innkeeper of the Year award?
Sid:	*No. Excuse me. I've got a business to run.*

Christmas Day in the Bears' House

FATHER BEAR: If there's one day in the year I like, it's Christmas Day. Don't you agree, Mother Bear? Mother Bear? Where's Mother Bear, Baby Bear?

BABY BEAR: In the kitchen washing up the porridge bowls, Dad.

FATHER BEAR: Good, good. Doesn't do to let them pile up, eh? Ah, here she comes now. I was just saying, Mother Bear, Christmas Day is very nice, isn't it?

MOTHER BEAR: For those of us who can sit down it is, yes.

FATHER BEAR: Yes, it's nice to spend time together as a loving family. Stop doing that to the carpet, Baby Bear, or I'll clip your ear. Is that cup of tea for me?

MOTHER BEAR: No. Me. I thought I'd have a rest. I've just chopped the wood, got the coal in, swept up the pine-needles, fed the cat, wrapped Goldilocks' present, taken the dog for a walk, and mended the fairy lights.

FATHER BEAR: And made the beds, I hope? We are expecting a visitor, don't forget. Ah me, this is the life. I love all this lazing around in my too-hard chair. Soon be time for another bowlful of that turkey-flavoured porridge, don't you think, Mother Bear? And make it too hot this time, will you? You know that's how I like it. What's the matter *now*, Baby Bear? Why are you whining?

BABY BEAR: When's Goldilocks coming round with my present?

FATHER BEAR: Dear, dear. Why are you so impatient? Don't you get enough toys? What happened to the shockproof, dustproof, porridge-proof, all-singing, all-dancing unbreakable watch I gave you for Christmas?

BABY BEAR: I lost it.

FATHER BEAR: Dear me, I don't know what young bears are coming to. When I was a little bear, I looked after my things.

MOTHER BEAR: Here's your porridge.

FATHER BEAR: Ah. Yum yum. [*Tastes it*] Yuck! This is disgusting!

MOTHER BEAR: I must have mixed the turkey flavour porridge with the pudding flavour one. Well, well, fancy that. However did I do such a thing . . .?

Pudding Play

CUSTOMER: Christmas pudding, please.

WAITRESS: Cream or custard?

CUSTOMER: Cream, please.

WAITRESS: Sorry, we're out of cream. You'll have to have it without custard. That'll be £5.

CUSTOMER: £5? That's a *terrible* price for Christmas Pudding.

WAITRESS: Well, it's terrible Christmas pudding. By the way, are you coming to the party?

CUSTOMER: Party? What party? When?

WAITRESS: On Friday. One of the mince pies is eight years old on Friday. Oh well, suit yourself. I'll just go and get your pudding.

CUSTOMER: I don't want it now.

WAITRESS: I'm sorry, you'll have to. It'll be terribly upset if you don't have it. That's the trouble with Christmas pudding. It gets so steamed up.

CUSTOMER: I don't care. Just bring me coffee. Two lumps.

WAITRESS: I'm sorry, we only have smooth.

CUSTOMER: I meant sugar.

WAITRESS: Oh, you shouldn't eat that stuff. Do you know, every time I eat sugar, I get a lump in my throat.

THE END. BOTH ACTORS TAKE BOWS TO RAPTUROUS APPLAUSE

Jokes

What do you call a clever snowman?
A snow all!

What do snowmen do when it freezes?
Grit their teeth!

What's white and goes up?
A stupid snowflake!

Heard about the snowman who sat on the radiator?
He made a complete pool of himself!

Kissing snowmen leaves me cold!

What do you call a snowball that's been knighted?
A noble snowble!

What do you call a ten-foot snowball-throwing yeti who's been knighted?
Sir!

What's tied up with ribbon and keeps you awake at night?
Rapping paper!

(Mean) Deer Definitions

Deer-anged – Rudolph's stupid story about leading the sleigh.

Deer-ision – What us deers give to Rudolph.

Deer-matitis – Nasty deerskin lurgy. Probably what caused Rudolph's red nose, ha ha.

Celebrity Interview with The Tooth Fairy

Interviewer: So, what's your problem? I understand you've got reservations about Christmas.

Fairy: *Not Christmas itself. Let me make that very clear. No, there's nothing wrong with Christmas. I've never had anything but the greatest respect for Santa. No, it's the sweets. Far too many sweets get eaten, loads of teeth fall out. The cry goes up, 'Call in the Tooth Fairies,' and then all hell breaks loose and it's goodbye spare time. We have to get straight up from the dinner* *table and rush off out before we've even had time to pull a cracker. And do we get a word of thanks? Do we heck. It's very selfish.*

Interviewer: Strong words. The Easter Bunny doesn't feel like you.

Fairy: *The least said about the Easter Bunny the better. Chocolate on the brain, that animal.*

Interviewer: Do you have anything else to say to our readers?

Fairy: *Yes. If you can't brush after every meal – comb! Remember that many a true word is spoken through false teeth. Be true to your teeth or they will be false to you! Watch out for the five pences in the Christmas pudding. Beware of all that sugar in the fizzy drinks, and above all, DON'T EAT TOFFEE.*

Interviewer: You're very single minded, aren't you?

Fairy: *Not at all. Tell me, do you have any cavities?*

Interviewer: Er . . .?

Fairy: *I knew it. You talk with an echo. You should get them fixed. There's only one thing that draws teeth painlessly, and that's a pencil.*

Interviewer: Very funny.

Fairy: *He who laughs last usually has a tooth missing. Now, instead of three helpings of Christmas pud followed by the top layer of the Family Choc Assortment, why not try a delicious stick of healthy celery followed by a crunchy carrot, blah blah . . .*

37

Christmas Top Ten

1 I'm Dreaming of a Green Christmas *Holly and the Ivys* (*Greenogram*)

2 There's No Business Like Snow Business *The Snowmen* (*ICY*)

3 Singin' in the Rain (Dear) *Dasher, Prancer, Donner and Blitzen* (*Deersound*)

4 I Saw Free Chips *Greasy Ray and the Deep Fries* (*Fish*)

5 Hot, Hot, Hot *The Chimneys* (*Smokestack*)

6 Ain't No Rooftop High Enough *Santa and the Sleighbells* (*Deersound*)

7 Only Three More Chopping Days to Christmas *The Woodmen* (*CHOP*)

8 Why, Oh Why, Oh Why? *The Three Whys' Men* (*Sagesound*)

9 I Lost My Tooth at Christmas Dinner *The Tough Turkeys* (*Gobblesound*)

10 Cold Snowman Blues *Snowman Joe* (*ICY*)

Christmas Day in the House of Bricks

PORKY: Well, here we all are, all four of us – Mother Pig and us three little pigs – the whole family together again, enjoying Christmas dinner. And all thanks to me.

TUBBY: Oh, not *that* again. He's on about *that* again.

TROTTER: Take no notice of him, Mother. He's just showing off.

PORKY: Well, you have to admit that if it wasn't for me you'd both be first course on the Wolf's Christmas dinner menu right now. And I might point out that

it'd be a chilly Christmas if we were having it at either one of *your* houses, ha ha, seeing as they're both flattened. Talking of houses, what d'you think of it, Mother Pig? The house?

MOTHER PIG: Oh – er – very nice. Very sturdy. Very modern. Although, of course, call me old-fashioned, but I prefer the traditional sty really. Try as I will, I can't get used to the idea of duvets. Give me a bit of mud-soaked, evil-smelling straw any time.

PORKY:	I'm having a Wolf Alarm fitted after Christmas. And I've had extra chains fitted on the door. And the roof's reinforced, naturally. I'm pretty certain that the house is now one hundred per cent huff-puffproof. You can't be too careful, oh dear me, no. Of course, Tubby and Trotter think otherwise. They don't think security matters.
TUBBY:	Listen to him.
TROTTER:	Mr Smug.
PORKY:	You're both jealous. Just because I'm the one with brains.

TROTTER: You were just lucky, that's all. It was just luck the man happened to be carrying some bricks when it was *your* turn to ask. If he'd been carrying pipe-cleaners you would have had some, wouldn't he, Tubby?

TUBBY: Course he would. [*Imitates*] 'Please, man, can I have some pipe-cleaners? I want to build a house.'

PORKY: Oh, shut up.

TROTTER: [*Warming to his theme*] I reckon if it'd been *jelly* he'd have had some, he's that stupid.

MOTHER: Oh, boys, boys, do stop your arguing. Let's all make friends, pull a cracker, throw another bucket of slop in the trough and put a pot of water to boil on the fire.

PORKY: Why do we need water?

MOTHER: Because someone's coming down the chimney – and I DON'T THINK IT'S SANTA!

[*Panic all round*]

Christmas Fudge by Witch Sludgegooey

My recipe for Christmas Fudge
Is really quite delicious.
My Christmas Fudge will never budge,
But sticks like glue to dishes.

I always make it every year
(A family tradition).
I offer it to visitors,
Who view it with suspicion.

I tell them of its yumminess
And they express their doubt.
It sits around for months and months
And then I throw it out.

Recipe
Ingredients
1 bucket sludge (fresh from ditch)
1 tin black treacle
1 pkt Witchways Economy-sized Instant Kwik-
    gel Fudge Mix
Strawberry flavouring

Method

1 Delicately throw all ingredients together.
2 Leave to mature in bucket.
3 Scoop on to plates.
4 Offer to friends.
5 Insist.
6 Act hurt and throw temper tantrum.
7 Give up.
8 Return to bucket.
9 Leave lying around collecting dust and small insects for best part of following year.
10 Throw out on Christmas Eve and make new batch.

Christmas Day in the Gingerbread House

ESMERELDA: You know, Drusilla, I'm glad you came round. Somehow I didn't fancy Christmas Day on me own this year.

DRUSILLA: Oh? Why's that, then, Es?

ESMERELDA: I dunno. I been a bit depressed over the last week. Here, have some more rat pie.

DRUSILLA: I shouldn't, but I will. After all, it is Christmas. I like the way you decorated it. The tail all coiled round the holly like that. Artistic, like.

ESMERELDA: Ta. Yes, I been feelin' a bit glum.

DRUSILLA: What, still broodin' about lettin' them kids escape, I suppose. 'Ansel and Gretel or whatever their names was.

ESMERELDA: You said it. It's been playin' on me mind something rotten. I just can't fathom out how I let 'em get away like that. I must be slippin'. I mean, lettin' 'em push me inside me own oven. Me *own oven*! That's what gets to me.

DRUSILLA: Don't you think you're gettin' a bit – obsessed, like? I mean, it was months ago.

ESMERELDA: I beg your pardon?

DRUSILLA: Nothing, nothing. I'm just saying we all makes mistakes. Any more o' that frog with brandy sauce?

ESMERELDA: Help yourself.

DRUSILLA: I will. After all, it is Christmas.

ESMERELDA: What gets me is, they don't even send me a Christmas card. After all the damage they did to me gutterin'. I had to have all the sugarplums replaced, you know. A fortune, it cost me.

DRUSILLA: It would. Sweet replacement does cost. I remember when you 'ad that double-glazed barley sugar put in. Would have kept me in Dried Stoat Mix for a year, what you paid. You should live in a cave, like me. Less overheads.

ESMERELDA: I don't like caves. They're just not me. I've spent years gettin' this house right. I'm still waitin' for just the right Liquorice Allsort to finish off

49

the porch. I've only just
finished pebble-dashin' the
walls with hundreds and
thousands. This house is my
life's work. Are you sayin' I
should move out?

DRUSILLA: No, no, don't get on your high
horse. Are those mince pies
slug or maggot?

ESMERELDA: Maggot.

DRUSILLA: Ooh, lovely. I'll have one. After
all, it is Christmas. Come on,
Es, lighten up a bit. Pull a
cracker. Forget the bloomin'
kids and enjoy yerself. After
tea, we'll light the cauldron,
get the wands out, eh? Do a bit
of cacklin'. Eh? What you say?

ESMERELDA: You're right, Drusilla. It
doesn't do to brood.

BOTH: After all, it is Christmas!

Nursery Rhymes With a Difference

Little Jack Horner

Little Jack Horner
Sat in a corner
Eating his Christmas Pie.
He put in his thumb
And pulled out a
Black widow spider with eight hairy legs
And said . . .
'AAAAAAAARGH! All right, who's the joker?'

Moral: You can't trust anyone.

Old Mother Hubbard

Old Mother Hubbard
Went to the cupboard
To get her poor dog a crumb,
But when she got there the cupboard was
    bare,
So the dog bit her hard on the bum.

She went to the hat shop to buy him a hat,
But when she got back he was tickling the cat.

She went to the fruit shop to buy him some
    fruit,
But when she got back he was smelling of Brut.

She went to the butcher's to buy him some
    meat,
But when she got back he was ripping a sheet.

She went to the laundry to get back his pants,
But when she got back he had just left for
    France.

And who can blame him? All he wanted was a
    bone.

*Moral: Don't have an animal if you can't look
    after it properly. Remember – a pet is for
    life, not just for Christmas!*

The North Wind Doth Blow

The north wind doth blow
And we shall have snow
And what will poor Robin do then, poor chap?

He'll wear woolly tights
And cut down on fights
And huddle in Marian's lap, poor chap!

*Moral: Don't camp out in Sherwood Forest in
    winter.*

Jack and Jill

Jack and Jill slid down the hill.
Fast they went, and faster,
Straight into an icy pond,
Which was a real disaster.

Jack got out and ran about
To help his circulation,
He didn't help poor Jill at all,
Though she was his relation.

Walking back, the cruel Jack
Was eaten by a bear-o.
Considering how mean he'd been
I think that's pretty fair-o.

*Moral: Don't abandon your sister in a frozen
    pond, or a polar bear will get you. (Pretty
    obvious really!)*

Celebrity Interview with Scrooge

Interviewer: What do you do when it's cold at Christmas?

Scrooge: *To save on heating, I huddle over a candle.*

Interviewer: What if it's *very* cold?

Scrooge: *I light it. Lend us five pounds.*

Interviewer: Why should I?

Scrooge: *I want to put it in the fridge. I like to have cold cash handy. Here's one for you. What's gold and silver and climbs trees?*

Interviewer: What?

Scrooge: *Money. I lied about it climbing trees. Did you know I was invited to a party the other day? I didn't know what to do. I didn't want to go empty-handed.*

Interviewer: So what did you do?

Scrooge: *I wore gloves. Fingerless ones, of course. Standard Miser.*

Interviewer: What's on your stocking list?

Scrooge: *Gold, a piggy bank, a calculator, an abacus, scales, a new wall safe, more gold, a new wallet, a thousand pounds and a decent burglar-alarm system. Oh, and gold. Did I mention that?*

Interviewer: Have you forgotten you owe me five pounds?

Scrooge: *Not yet. Give me time and I will. I hate to part with money. Oh, money, money, lovely money.*

Interviewer: What's so good about being a skinflint?

Scrooge: *The money. How d'you kill a miser?*

Interviewer: I don't know. How?

Scrooge: *Throw two pence under a bus. Ha ha. You thought we misers had no sense of humour, didn't you? You don't have to believe everything that writer chappy says about me, you know. What the dickens was his name again?*

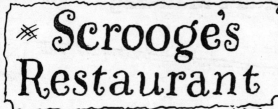

Scrooge's Restaurant

Christmas Menu

Starter:
Cold boiled ham
(ham boiled in cold water)

Main Course:
Poor Man's Turkey (stuffed with newspaper),
served with our chef's delicious Yo-yo Christmas
Special (piece of spaghetti wrapped around
a sprout)

Dessert:
Scrooge's Christmas Pudding
(three slices stale bread, thimbleful sugar, three
currants chopped fine, $1/2$ oz old chip fat)

A Miserly Christmas to all our
customers

Candle extra
SERVICE NOT INCLUDED

Santa's Mail-bag

Dear Santa

I want a helicopter, my bike fixed and my violin busted.

Reluctant Fiddler
Hull

Dear Santa

Kindly leave the following in my Christmas stocking. A house in the South of France, a Porsche, a luxury yacht, a private plane, a swimming-pool, bags of money and an orange. Thanking you in advance.

Greedy Vegetarian
Birmingham

Dear Santa

For Christmas, I would like to ban what I call the ten Ps. Namely:

Presents
Parties
Popular music
Plum pudding
Prattish dancing
Particularly noisy squeakers, toy trumpets, etc.
Perfectly awful silly hats
Persistent joke-telling
Pickled onions
Pine-needles

Yours sincerely

Major Spoilsport
Surrey

PS I personally will be spending my time marching up and down complaining about children today. It's a pity more people don't do the same.

Dear Santa

I've always admired your lovely beard. It looks in such good condition. Is it real, or is it a false one? If false, could you possibly tell me where to get one and if I should wash it or get it dry-cleaned. I like your beard so much, I have written a poem about it.

Would I look weird
In Santa's beard?
Probably.

Beard Fan
Stamford

Dear Santa

I can't help noticing how you appear to keep changing shape. Why, only the other day I saw you in a grotto in Plymouth, looking quite tubby and ringing a bell. Then, only two days later, when up staying with my sister, Mrs Freda Bryant of Crouch End, I saw you again outside Woolies – and I was alarmed and amazed to see that you had lost three stone in weight and a foot in height and gained about twenty years. Your beard also appeared much longer. I know a lot can be achieved by the use of cushions and mirrors, but this seems ridiculous! Are you sure you're eating properly?

Mrs Brenda Nugent
Swansea

P.S My sister Freda has just rung me to say that she saw you again today; you were over six feet tall and getting into a Ford Cortina. Are we seeing things? Do people know something we don't know?

P.S How do you manage all those chimneys in one night?

61

Dear Santa

Please can I have a Do-it-yourself book, a new saw, a new hammer and a year's supply of Elastoplast?

Yours tooly

Andy Mann
Hammersmith

Dera snta

Waht i wnt forrrr Chrismus is a neew typr%ter. ths one macks too manny miztakes. a!ls0 the O is uppsid downe.)plese dotn sugest i uze ritink papper. the truobel iz wiht pappe,r, no mater how i moove it, = it alwys remans stationery:

yrs fathfule

Al Thumbbs
Newcatsle

Dear Santa

I would like a new watch for Christmas. I left my old one upstairs and it ran down. Then the dog ate it, which was time-consuming. Luckily he sicked it up, but it doesn't look well and I feel its hours are numbered.

Yours

Mr Dick Tock
Aylesbury

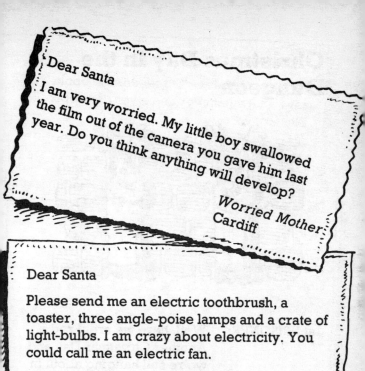

Dear Santa

I am very worried. My little boy swallowed the film out of the camera you gave him last year. Do you think anything will develop?

Worried Mother
Cardiff

Dear Santa

Please send me an electric toothbrush, a toaster, three angle-poise lamps and a crate of light-bulbs. I am crazy about electricity. You could call me an electric fan.

Ms Flicka de Switch
Brighton

Dear Santa

Why does Christmas always come when the stores are so crowded? I spent five hours in one shop. Mind you, my coat was caught in the lift at the time.

Puzzled
Islington

Christmas Day in the Dungeon

1st PRISONER: Well, here we are, Fred. Another Christmas Day and we're still hanging about in this dungeon. Oh well, I suppose we should make the best of it.

2nd PRISONER: You've got to admit the jailer made an effort this year though, Terry. The paper-chains and that.

1st PRISONER: Oh I do, I do. Credit where it's due. And the sprig of holly on the dish of old mashed potato for Christmas Eve was a nice touch, I thought.

2nd PRISONER: Here's my present to you, by the way.

1st PRISONER: Oh, fur-lined shackles! How kind. Just what I wanted. Here's mine to you.

2nd PRISONER: Oh, great! Matching leg-irons. Perfect. Thanks, Terry. Now, what have we got for Christmas lunch this year, I wonder, eh? Ooh, look. What a fantastic treat! A lovely, nourishing jug of life-giving water – and a whole sandwich between us! What filling is it, Terry?

1st PRISONER: Bread, I think, Fred.

2nd PRISONER: Oh, really? I was hoping it might be wood. I love club sandwiches.

1st PRISONER: I kinda wished it was bone. I've always been partial to a knuckle sandwich. Oh well. Hey! Wait a minute! What's this?

2nd PRISONER: It's a piece of cheese from the rat trap! Oh thank you, thank you. Whoever said the jailer didn't have a heart?

1st PRISONER: Oh he does, he does. I used to hang upside down, remember? I talked to him about it and he really straightened me out.

1st PRISONER: Yes, he's not a bad sort. I'd go so far as to say he's really spoiling us this year. Tell you what, let's save this wonderful feast till later. You never know. Leave it another hour or so, and the sandwich might have grown a bit more mould! More to go round, eh?

2nd PRISONER: You're right. We've had a super day so far. Maybe our luck will hold. In the mean time, let's sip our water and sing some jolly Christmas songs.

TOGETHER: [*Sing*] Oh, it's fun spending Christmas in the dungeon. It's great to be hanging on the wall . . .

All-purpose 'Disgusted' Form

Please tick appropriate box and post up chimney

I am very disappointed with the:

pink plastic sewing-machine with missing handle ☐
Do-it-yourself Junior Surgery kit ☐
Plinkalong Tinkletonkle baby-walker ☐
chainsaw ☐
Toothpaste Top Collector's Guide 1984 ☐
walnut ☐

. . . I received in my stocking this year. As far as I am concerned, a present like this is much too:

cheap and nasty ☐
painful ☐
insultingly babyish ☐
highly dangerous ☐
exceedingly dull ☐
small ☐

I see no evidence of the:

jumbo jet ☐
sweet shop ☐
sports car ☐
astronaut's licence ☐
ice-cream van ☐
bags of gold ☐

. . . I asked for. Could these have been omitted in error? Anyway, I will definitely be taking the matter:

further ☐
seriously ☐
up with the relevant authorities ☐
up in the press ☐
up the chimney ☐

Please rectify as soon as possible.

Name _____

Address _____

_____

_____

Stocking description _____

Christmas Books

PREPARING CHRISTMAS DINNER — Stefan de Turkey

CHRISTMAS IS A PINE IN THE NECK (A TREE'S PERSPECTIVE) — Bruce Spruce

CHRISTMAS FUN! — Paula Cracker and Ava Larff

The Pantomime Villain — Sssssssid Boooooon

Recycling your Mince Pies — Stella Lotova

Christmas Appeal · Ada Charity

NEVER KISS A SNOWMAN — I.C. Lipps

Make Your Own Decorations

Miles O'Paperchains

Bill Zaplenti

After Christmas

The VANISHING TURKEY

Henrietta Lott

The PLEASURE of a REAL FIRE

COLAN ~DE~ CARPET

The Night I Hit a Chimney

RUDOLPH THE BLACK-EYED REINDEER

Christmas Day in the Wolf's Den

WOLF: Hello? . . . Is that the Big Bad Wolf's house? . . . It is? . . . This is his cousin, Rory . . . Yes, that's right, the not-quite-so-Big Bad Wolf . . . Yes, yes, the one that ate Red Riding Hood's granny. That one. Can I speak to him please? . . . He's not there? . . . He's off out after the three little pigs again? But it's Christmas Day! . . . What? He's got an especially cunning plan? Well, maybe so, but he was supposed to be coming round to my house for Christmas lunch, it was all arranged. Everything's ready. I've just got to make the brandy sauce. How am I

supposed to eat it all myself? . . . Oh,
never mind . . . No, no message . . .
[*Puts down receiver*]

[*Crossly*] Honestly, you go to all the
trouble . . . [*Picks up, redials*]

Hello? . . . Is that the Fox residence?
. . . [*Puts down receiver*]

If there's one thing I can't abide, it's
answer machines. Especially joke
ones recorded by a chicken. [*Sighs*]
Now, let me see, who else is there?
. . . ah . . . [*Redials*]

Hello? . . . Is that the famous-but-unpopular Animals Residential Home? . . . I wonder if I might speak to King Kong? . . . Oh dear, really? Gone to the jungle to see his gran, you say? What a pity. What about Sylvester? . . . I see. Invited to lunch with Tweety Pie. Hmm. What about the crocodile in Peter Pan? . . . Gone out? . . . Back in a tick? . . . no, that'll be too late, I need someone now really, everything's getting spoiled . . . Oh, never mind, I'll try elsewhere . . . [*Slams phone down*]

That's it. I've tried everyone I can think of. That's the trouble with being a baddy. No one ever wants to spend Christmas Day with you. Oh well. If I have to, I have to. [*Dials*]

Hello? . . . Red Riding Hood? . . .

Do-it-yourself Pantomime

SLEEPING GOOSE
**a pantomime for all the family
to be performed after opening the presents
and before lunch**

The Producer – You

The Cast:
Spirit of the pantomime – Grandad
Fairy Godmother – Gran
Cinderella – Mum
Prince Charming – Dad
Ugly stepsisters – Uncle Maurice and Uncle
    Dave
Mother Goose – Aunty Shirley
Other parts – various cousins, small brothers
    and sisters, cat, etc.

A blasted heath. Enter Spirit of the pantomime in cardboard crown and carpet slippers. He is looking for his pipe.

SPIRIT: Our panto is about to start
        And everyone will have a part.
        It starts upon a blasted heath,
        Where someone searches for her
            teeth.

[*Enter Fairy Godmother, looking for her teeth*]

FAIRY GODMOTHER:
        I could have sworn I put them in.
        Oh, never mind. Let me begin.

[*She sees Cinderella*]

        Now tell me, Cinders, tell me true,
        That cardigan I knitted you,
        It took the best part of a year,
        But you do like it not, I fear.

CINDERELLA:
        The garment fills me with delight
        Although it is a wee bit tight.
        And shocking pink is not quite me.

FAIRY GODMOTHER:
        She doesn't like it. There, you see?

SPIRIT: I wonder where I left my pipe.
        I am a most forgetful type.

[*Enter Prince Charming*]

PRINCE: Oh, look! Who can this maiden be?
Say, what a lovely sight is she!
I wonder if her smile will stay
When she hears what I have to say.

[*To Cinderella*]

I bring you tragic news, my dear
The oven wasn't on, I fear
The goose is raw as raw can be.

CINDERELLA: [*Sharply*]
Blame someone else. Just don't blame
me.
I'm tired of doing all the work
When others sit about and shirk.

78

PRINCE: Our Christmas dinner is no more!
It opened up the oven door
And clambered down and
waddled out.

CINDERELLA:
I won't discuss it if you shout.

PRINCE: The question is, what shall we do?

CINDERELLA:
Why should I care? It's up to you.

PRINCE:
I'll wave my sword and save the day.

CINDERELLA:
Just put your stupid sword away.

[*Enter Ugly stepsisters*]

DRUSILLA: Oh, Cinderella! There you are!

PRISCILLA: Scrub the kitchen!

DRUSILLA: Clean the car!

PRISCILLA: Hoist the main brace!

DRUSILLA: Slice the sluice!

PRISCILLA: Heat the oven!

DRUSILLA: Catch the goose!

79

PRISCILLA: Cook our lunch and make it
             snappy.

CINDERELLA: Woe is me, I'm so unhappy.

[*Exit Cinderella in tears of exhaustion*]

[*Stepsisters do silly dance wearing saucepan
lids and fright wigs*]

[*Enter Mother Goose*]

MOTHER GOOSE:
             I do not like this pantomime.
             Oh, goodness me, is that the time?
             I must escape – 'tis not my fate
             To end in gravy on a plate.

[*Exit Mother Goose, chased by Fairy
Godmother, Prince, Cinderella, Ugly
stepsisters, assorted pantomime cows, cats
and horses, etc.*]

SPIRIT: [*Waking with a start*] Eh? Oh –

          And now our tale is nearly done.
          We hope you have enjoyed the fun.
          I thought it was a load of tripe,
          But there you go. Ah, *there's* my
          pipe!

                [*Curtain*]

Pantomime Audition Jokes

PRODUCER: [*To seven dwarfs*] Have any of you had any stage experience?

GRUMPY: *No, but Sneezy had his leg in a cast once.*

'NEXT PLEASE.'

PRODUCER: We want you to dress up as a chunk of bread filled with cheese, ham pickle, chutney, tomato, lettuce, cucumber, onions and mayonnaise.

ROBIN HOOD: *I'll do it. It sounds like a big roll.*

'NEXT PLEASE.'

PRODUCER: Are you new to show business?

SNOW WHITE: *Oh no. I've always had the*
               theatre in my veins.
               Sometimes I wish I had
               blood.

               'NEXT PLEASE.'

PRODUCER: Did you start out as an actor?

DICK WHITTINGTON: *No, as a little boy.*

               'NEXT PLEASE.'

PRODUCER: You'll have to climb this sixty-
             foot beanstalk.

JACK: *Gosh! That's a tall order.*

               'NEXT PLEASE.'

PRODUCER: So you're happy to play the
pumpkin?

PUMPKIN: *Certainly. You can really get your
teeth into a part like that.*

'NEXT PLEASE.'

PRODUCER: Are you happy to get the part of
the pantomime cow?

COW: *Yes. I shall milk it for all it's worth.*

'NEXT PLEASE.'

PRODUCER: So, little birdy, you want to be
Mother Goose, eh? Can you
talk?

GOOSE: *Yeah, I can talk. Can you fly?*

'NEXT PLEASE.'

83

PRODUCER: Have you ever played Puss in
Boots?

PUSS: *No but I've done it in Woolworth's.*

'NEXT PLEASE.'

PRODUCER: I'm sorry, we don't need a
pantomime camel.

CAMEL: *Oh, sir, sir, give me a job, do!*
Before I got into show business, my
life was one big desert . . .

Quiz

So You Want To Be a Pantomime Star?
But how suitable are you? How much do you
really know about panto? Fill in our quiz and
find out!

1 You don't *really* want to star in panto, do
   you?

      a)   Oh yes I do   ☐
      b)   Oh no you don't ☐
      c)   Oh yes I do   ☐
      d)   Oh no you don't ☐
      e)   Oh yes I do   ☐

2 If Snow White melted in the Prince's arms,
   was she then known as Slush Grey?

      a)   Yes   ☐
      b)   No   ☐

3 If the seven dwarfs applied for a job, would they all get on the short list?

      a)   Yes   ☐
      b)   No   ☐

4 Why is it usually the front end of the panto horse that signs the autographs?

a)   The front end's got the horse sense   ☐
b)   The back end's got the bum writing   ☐

5 A pantomime cow is expected to be moosical.

      a)   True   ☐
      b)   False   ☐
      c)   Pull the udder one   ☐

6 Have you ever tried to put a Puss in Boots?

a)   Yes   ☐
b)   No   ☐
c)   Are you kidding? Mine won't even be put through the cat-flap!   ☐

7 Select the best name for a pantomime
   Dame:

a) Dame Splishy Splashy ☐
b) Widow Hanky Panky ☐
c) Old Mother Scrubadub ☐
d) Her Royal Majesty Queen Elizabeth II ☐

8 Do you know the following community
   songs?

a) 'She left her electric blanket on, and now
   she's the Toast of the Town'
                Yes ☐   No ☐

b) 'Don't stick yer head in the laundry bag,
   you might get a sock in the mouth'
                Yes ☐   No ☐

c) 'I'll meet you under the clothes line, cos
   that's where I hang out'
                Yes ☐   No ☐

9 What is the correct response when the
   villain appears?

a) Boo ☐
b) Hiss ☐
c) Hooray ☐
d) He's behind you! ☐
e) Isn't that the man from the fish shop in
   a black wig? ☐

10 If the Dame is really a man and the
    principle boy is really a girl, what does
    that make the pantomime cow?

      a)   A bull   ☐
      b)   Confused   ☐

11 Here is the verse of a typical pantomime
    song. Please provide the missing word.

    Ooh, Mother! Whoops, me knickers!
    Caught them in the mangle!
    Everyone needs knickers
    For the naughty bits that _____.

12 I WOULD LIKE TO STAR IN PANTO
    BECAUSE: (Tick the correct answer)

a) I can't resist the roar of the greasepaint
    and the smell of the crowds (or is it the
    other way round?)   ☐

b) All right, I'll come clean. I want to be a
    soap star.   ☐

So, what do you think? Are you suitable? We
wouldn't know, we've never met you!

Christmas Day in the Dragon's Lair

DRAGON: You know, George, I'm really
glad I invited you over. It's time
we let bygones be bygones, don't
you think? Season of goodwill and
all that. Dang! Just burnt me claw
on that oven! Pass me a bucket of
water, would you – oops, wait a
minute! Pass the fire extinguisher.
I've had another slight accident;
bit of a cough, set fire to the
curtains, ha ha, not to worry – oh,
drat! Now I've gone and burnt the
turkey. Oops! Nearly set fire to
the oven gloves. My, what a mad
cave this is. Over here, George,
quick as you can. I think the sofa's
starting to smoulder. Why's the

oven dinging like that? Oh dear
. . . just remembered . . . hope you
like charred Christmas pudding
. . . No, it's all right, George, you
don't need to ring the fire
brigade. Everything's under
control . . . my, it's hot in here.
What's this? My Christmas
present? Oh, George, you
shouldn't have . . . why, it's a
book. *Safety in the Cave* by Hugh
Burntit. Why, how thoughtful.

Santa's School Report

Lapland Junior School

Name: <u>Nicholas (St)</u>

Class: <u>3a</u>

English: Writing poor, mainly because he won't take his mittens off. However, the dear boy does his best. I'd like a new mortar-board, a waistcoat, some Liquorice Allsorts and a monogrammed fountain-pen.

Reindeer Management: Brilliant. Nicky has a real magic touch with the reindeer. I'd go so far as to say that one day, he'll make his career with deer. And when he does, I'd like a new dressing-gown, Trivial Pursuit and the new Cliff Richard single.

Maths: Excellent, especially if it's a problem involving a herd of reindeer, a load of buckets and a shovel. And what he doesn't know about the world-wide distribution of small plastic toys you could write on a gift-tag. I'd like a new pencil-box, bath salts and a solar calculator.

PE: His performance when moving up and down in a confined space (i.e. chimneys) has been outstanding. Quite frankly, I don't know how he does it. It's uncanny what young Nicky can squeeze that tubby little tummy into. I want some new trainers, a punch-bag, and tickets for the Gunners.

Music: Shows some promise on the bells, but not much else. Tends to horse around during singing lessons – or should I say 'deer around', ha ha? I think it's true to say that young Nicholas only likes songs with Ho-ho-ho in the chorus. Nevertheless, he's a pleasure to teach. Mine's a Stradivarius.

DT: I am very impressed with young
Nicholas's natural talent for toy-making. I
believe he has some future plan to make quite
a little business of it, delivering sackfuls free
of charge down all the chimneys in the land,
or some such childish scheme. Of course, it'll
never catch on, but who am I to dampen his
youthful enthusiasm? Travel Scrabble, new
underpants, a new tennis racket and a year's
supply of Maltesers, please.

Class teacher's comments: A credit to the
class. A digital watch, a motorized lawn-mower
and a new tie should do me nicely.

Headteacher's comments: In general I am
very impressed with young Nicholas's
progress. I'd say he was destined to be a
high-flyer. Make mine a huge black Jaguar, a
large box of truffles and early retirement.
Thank you very much.

Potty Poetry

What I Want for Christmas by Dan Druff

What I want for Christmas?
Well, shampoo is what I say.
I've got this shocking dandruff
And it just won't go away.

I've tried a million remedies,
But nothing makes it go.
In the very midst of summer,
On my shoulders there is snow.

There's nothing I can do at all.
The problem's simply shocking.
So if you want to please me,
Pop some shampoo in my stocking.

Now, shall I write another verse
Or shall I leave it there?
I've done enough. I'll post it off
And then I'll wash my hair.

The Back Legs of the Panto Horse

I'm the back legs of the panto horse,
But no one knows my name.
The front end gets the carrots,
The front end gets the fame.
The front is the mouth end
And always hogs the spot,
While all I do is swish my tail
And trot, trot, trot, trot, trot.

I'm the back legs of the panto horse,
But no one seems to care.
The front end gets the credit
And I don't think that's fair.
The front gets the flowers
And curtseys quite a lot,
But all I do is swish my tail
And trot, trot, trot, trot, trot.

I'm the back legs of the panto horse.
The front end gets the laughs
And all the praise and all the neighs
And signs the autographs.
But here, at the back end,
It's always dark and hot,
And all I do is swish my tail
And trot, trot, trot, trot, trot.

No Boots for Christmas

They couldn't afford to buy me boots.
(That's how it goes.)
Instead, they painted my feet black
(And laced my toes).

Christmas Day in the Workhouse

It was Christmas day in the workhouse
And poor little Benny was there.
His poor little hands were frozen,
His poor little feet were bare.
His poor little nose was running,
There were drops dripping from the end-o.
But poor little Ben didn't notice,
Because he'd got a Super Nintendo.

Celebrity Interview with Noah Parkin, Traffic Warden

Interviewer: So, Mr Parkin. How does it feel to be the warden responsible for giving Santa a parking ticket?

Noah: *Look, I got me job to do, right? There's rules. If there's double yellow lines, you shouldn't park there. I don't care if it's a limo, a Merc, or a sleigh with eight reindeer. Obey the rules, or get a ticket. That's my motto.*

Interviewer: But it *was* Christmas Eve. And Santa had his job to do as well. Weren't you just being a malicious misery with a spiteful urge to ruin the Christmas of all children everywhere?

Noah: *Well, yes, of course, naturally that came into it. But mainly it's because of the rules. I'm a stickler for rules I am. We all are in my family.*

Interviewer: So I've noticed. It was you, I take it, who clobbered the Snow Queen for failing to display a current tax disc?

Noah: [*Proudly*] *That was me. Quite nasty she got, too. Threatened*

98

to take me to her icy palace in the North and make me count icy splinters for eternity.
'Lady,' I said. 'Don't threaten me. You gotta problem, take it up with the proper authorities. Me, I gotta job to do.'

Interviewer: Was it you who had the wooden horse of Troy wheel clamped?

Noah: *That was me, yep. Terrible spoil-sport I am.*

Interviewer: And didn't you have Cinderella's pumpkin coach towed away?

Noah: *No, actually that was Ava Ticket, a cousin on my mother's side. But it was me that had Noddy towed away. Cheeky little so-and-so rang his bell at me. I threw the book at him. If it wasn't for Big Ears, he'd still be paying the fine now.*

Interviewer: So Santa's fine stands?

Noah: *It certainly does. Now, move along if you please. Unless you want to be clamped?*

Christmas Day TV Programmes

Saturday 25 December – Christmas Day

6.00 PORRIDGE NEWS:
A light-hearted start to the day over a bowl of porridge with Father Bear. Guests include Winnie the Pooh, the entire cast of *The Teddy Bear's Picnic* and Humphrey Beargart, star of *Kids, I Shrank the Honey*. Watch – if you can bear it.

7.00 KING COLE COMES CLEAN:
An in-depth interview with King Cole, who answers some burning questions about smokeless fuel and why his son Ashley is known as the Black Prince.

8.00 COOKING – WITH WITCH CATTRAP:
Popular cook, Witch Cattrap, reveals the secret ingredient of her Christmas pudding. Have your sick-bag ready.

9.00 SINGASONGACHRISTMAS:
Carols around the tree, presented by Carol Singer and Belle Ringer. Features Jilly Fingers, Rani Noses and Collette Tintin.

10.00 FILM: Gnome Alone:
The exciting tale of a gnome left all alone at Christmas time, who outwits two naughty pixies who try to break into his mushroom and steal his fishing-rod.

12.00 PRIME-TIME WRESTLING:
Giant Beanstalk v. Jack. A seasonal bout in which Jack gives away forty-two stone, but comes out on top.

12.30 UNEVEN-A-SIDE FOOTBALL:
The seven dwarfs against Godzilla. Should be a short game.

1.30 FILM: Mopey Dick:
The sensational story of one man's struggle
to cheer up a depressed whale.

3.00 THE WICKED QUEEN'S SPEECH:
Her Majesty once again addresses the nation
on the subject of who is the fairest of them all.
Be prepared for the annual tantrum.

Pet Presents

1 DOG SANTA HAT

What will the well-dressed dog be wearing
this Christmas? His very own Santa hat, that's
what! Your dog might only be a mongrel, but
he can really show those pedigrees something
when he's wearing his fun-look, fashionable
Santa hat.

Available in a choice of two colours, red and
white or white and red.

£4.99

2 FAKE REINDEER ANTLERS

Get your horse into the spirit of things by
buying him a hilariously realistic set of
reindeer antlers. Comes with a free red nose.

£25.99

3 WHACKY WOLF SHOWER-CAP

What better present to buy your sheep than
this whacky wolf shower-cap. Exhibitionists
even wear them to the sheep-dip! Made from
latex rubber, one size fits all.

£9.99

Celebrity Interview with the Christmas-tree Fairy

Interviewer: Do you like being the Christmas-tree fairy?

Fairy: *Twa la, twa la la, why, of course I do! Wouldn't you?* [Simpers, pouts, bats eyelashes, gives silvery laugh, points toes prettily and tosses golden ringlets]

Interviewer: Why?

Fairy: *Because I wear a white dress and evewybody says how pwitty I am.* [Sings and dances] *I feel pwitty, oh so pwitty . . .*

Interviewer: You don't think, perhaps, you're a bit of a namby-pamby goody-goody?

Fairy: [Coldly] *I'm sowee? What did you say?*

Interviewer: I said, do you get a good view from the top of the tree?

Fairy: *Oh yes. And when it's midnight, I fly off the twee and flit about the woom, touching evewything with my silver wand and gwanting wishes.*

Interviewer: Will you grant my wish?

Fairy: *Why, of course I will. What is it?*

Interviewer: Just fly under my boot for a moment . . .

Christmas Day in the Shoe

OLD WOMAN: Wayne, get off that sofa! Maureen, you know what'll happen if you do that to the baby again. Tracey, I've told you a million times to *PUT THAT DOWN!* Doreen, give Kevin his teddy back! Wayne, get off that sofa! Jason, give little Stevie his broth without any bread, and make sure he doesn't spill it all down himself! Oh, there now! Clumsy boy! He's spilt it all down himself. I told you to look what you were doing. Wayne, get off that sofa! Sandra, have you laid that table yet? Diane, will you please stop pestering me and let go of my apron-strings. Oh my goodness, the baby's eating the cat-food! Maureen, you were supposed to be looking after him. If it wasn't Christmas Day I'd whip you all soundly and send you to bed, you naughty children! Wayne, get off that sofa, etc . . .

Diary
of
Santa's
Little
Helper

Monday 18 December

Started work on assembly line! Same old gang here again. Turgleberry and Moonstar and Fairy Pipkin and Nimbleknees and Sean. Hah! Knew they'd be back. Last year they swore they'd never set foot in the place again unless the Boss doubled the nectar vouchers and installed an elderberry machine – but here they all are, hammering and sticking and painting away under the same old primitive conditions as though buttercups wouldn't melt in their mouths.

Mind you, so am I. Why, I ask myself? Oops! Here come the wooden soldiers! Better start painting.

Tuesday 19 December

I've remembered what it is I like so much about this job – it's the singing! Where better to sing traditional Elf work-songs than in Santa's workshop? I love singing. I have a wonderful voice. I once sang for the King of the Fairies. At least, he said he was. He said, 'If you're a good singer, I'm the King of the Fairies.' Yesterday I treated everyone to a medley, starting with 'Breakin' toys out here on the chain-gang' and ending with the tragic 'Lone Elf Blues'. As usual, my efforts were unappreciated. There are no music lovers in this workshop. They all complained to the Boss, and today I find I've been taken off soldiers and put on teddy bears. Actually, it's nice here in the teddy department. It's miles away from the main bit, all quiet and cosy, with lots of soft yellow fur everywhere. I almost think I could dozzzzz . . .

Wednesday 20 December

Got in late this morning. The Boss gave me a
funny look. I said, just as a little joke, 'Sorry
I'm late, but there's eight elves in our family
and the alarm was set for seven.' I don't think
he got it. 'I might get to work late,' I told him,
'but I make up for it by leaving early.' That
went down like a lead balloon. I've been taken
off teddies. Apparently I sing in my sleep.
Yesterday I sang a song called 'The Clock',
and really alarmed everybody (ha ha).

I'm now on Crackers, with Turgleberry and
Nimbleknees, worst luck! I hate it when those
two get together. They gang up. I told them I
was going away to study singing, and they
said, 'Good, how far away?' I told them I sang
with feeling, and they said if I had any feelings
I wouldn't sing. I'm going to put in an official
complaint.

Thursday 21 December

Thank goodness I'm not on Crackers any more.
The Boss was quite sympathetic when I asked
to be moved. I guess he knows what the others
are like. Mind you, I'm not much better off.
He's stuck me in the Noisy Toys room with
Sean, who keeps singing leprechaun ballads
at the top of his voice. I think he's trying to
drown me out. I don't let him, though. 'Gonna
jump down, turn around, picka bale a' cotton,
tra la . . .'

Friday 22 December

Hey ho, moved again. Actually, I like my latest job. Feeding the reindeer. Right on top of a mountain, miles from anywhere. Plenty of fresh air and the chance to sing to my heart's content. It's good to get out of that stuffy workshop, I can tell you. And I pride myself that I have a way with animals. Dasher and Prancer are getting to know the sound of my voice, and Blitzen starts rolling his eyes and pawing the ground with his hooves whenever he sees me.

Saturday 23 December

It's not much fun being trampled by a herd of reindeer, I can tell you. I'm writing this diary in my sick-bed, with great difficulty. Mind you, the nurses are very kind. Thank heaven for the National Elf Service. Turgleberry and that lot have just called by with some grapes. The Boss is coming later. He was first on the scene of the accident. He was very kind. He says he had no idea Cupid had such a thing about Elf work-songs. Apparently he was badly frightened by one as a young deer.

The Boss could see I was upset. Well, it's not surprising. Tomorrow's Christmas Eve. I've never missed a Christmas Eve in the last ten years. I mean, *it's the best bit!* The snow and the sleigh ride and the stockings and everything. D'you know, it's not like me at all, but right now I just don't feel like singing . . .

Sunday 24 December – The Big Night!

Well, here I am, right as rain again. Might have known the Boss'd sort me out. A wink of his eye, a snap of his fingers, and I was out of bed in a twinkling! Christmas Magic. The nurses said they'd never seen anything like it. I guess being a Little Helper does have its perks. Better stop now, and help load the sleigh.

One thing I've noticed. I've got this rotten sore throat. Hurts to sing. I keep trying to mention it to the Boss, but he seems a bit busy . . .

Santa's Little Helper Application Form

Name _____

Address _____

_____

_____

Date of Birth _____

Species (Imp, Gnome, Pixie, etc.) _____

Please tick the relevant boxes.

1 Are you a) small   ☐
           b) cute   ☐
           c) green   ☐
           d) other   ☐

2 Do you own
  a) a pointy hat   ☐
  b) a wand   ☐
  c) a mushroom   ☐
  d) a trained slug   ☐

3 Are you, or have you ever been, allergic to any of the following:
  a) soot   ☐
  b) reindeer hair   ☐
  c) mince pies   ☐
  d) children   ☐

4 Do you know the words to the following well-loved Santa's Little Helper work-songs:
  a) 'Dig, dig, dig'
    Yes ☐   No ☐
  b) 'Hammer, hammer, hammer'
    Yes ☐   No ☐
  c) 'Slog, slog, slog'
    Yes ☐   No ☐
  d) 'We shall overcome'
    Yes ☐   No ☐

5 What makes you wish to join Santa's work force? Is it:
  a) the chance to make little children happy   ☐
  b) the travel   ☐
  c) the opportunity to make new cute green friends   ☐
  d) the glamour   ☐
  e) the free mince pies   ☐

6 Complete the following sentence in no more than eighty words: I WOULD LIKE TO BE A SANTA'S LITTLE HELPER BECAUSE . . .

_____

_____

_____

_____

_____

_____

_____

_____

_____

_____

_____

Applicants should familiarize themselves with the words to the traditional Helper Song, which appear below:

1   I'm Santa's Little Helper,
    My name is Jolly Jack.
    And every day, I'm glad to say,
    I always get the sack.

    Chorus:
    Yes, his name is Jolly Jack,
    His name is Jolly Jack,
    He's Santa's Little Helper
    And he always gets the sack.

2   I'm Santa's Little Helper,
    My name is Fairy Bette.
    I always bring the reindeer,
    That's why I'm always wet.

    Chorus:
    Yes, her name is Fairy Bette, etc.

3   I'm Santa's Little Helper,
    My name is Brownie Brown.
    And I test out the chimneys,
    That's why I'm up and down.

    Chorus:
    Yes, his name is Brownie Brown, etc.

Famous Celebrities Tell Their New Year's Resolutions

Father Bear: To help Mother Bear more around the house, get more exercise, eat less porridge, fix Baby Bear's chair and install a decent burglar alarm.

Tarzan: To stop hanging around, get my hair cut, buy a nice pair of sensible shoes and get a proper jo-eeoeeo-eeoeeob! [*Do Tarzan call*]

Superman: Try to remember about the tights and the underpants . . . oh dear . . . it's like I've got this terrible blockage . . .

Cat Woman: To stop being so fussy about my food and check regularly for fur-balls.

The Lone Ranger: To search for new thrills and adventure and muck out Silver more regularly. Or perhaps I'll give up this dangerous life, hang up my mask, get myself a suit and work for a bank. I could call myself the Loan Arranger.

Red Riding Hood: Don't go off by myself, don't pick wild flowers, don't talk to strangers, don't believe what anyone tells me, get my sight and hearing tested and be kind to animals.

Red Riding Hood's Grandma: Remember to take my ginger wine more regularly. I've been feeling down in the mouth recently.

Attila the Hun: Pick on everyone, conquer the world and put up a shelf in the spare room.

Robin Hood: Defeat the sheriff, liberate the poor, marry Marian and mend that ladder in my tights.

Dracula: Stop biting my nails or I'll have no fingers left. Must tell Igor to get some more mustard . . .

The Incredible Hulk: Stop losing my temper. Resist swelling up, ruining my shirt and trousers, turning green and ripping people limb from limb. Instead, learn to sit quietly pouting in a corner and call myself the Incredible Sulk. Or slink around furtively and become known as the Incredible Skulk.

King Kong: Try and cut down on the bananas. Again.

Batman: New Year's resolution? Er – dunno dunno dunno dunno, dunno dunno dunno dunno, Batman! [*Sing signature tune*]

The Pirate Captain: Give up this wicked life and become a boxer. Swop the rum for the punch. At least I've got a great left hook. Pity about the wooden leg . . .

Sleeping Beauty: To try to get up in the mornings.

A Dragon: Try to get myself a job. Guarding something. Ideally, I'd like to guard a fort. I'd do it free cos it's not the money, it's the fort that counts.

Jumbo the Elephant: Count my blessings. Be thankful I don't have sinus trouble.

Only Three More Chopping Days to Christmas

There were only three more chopping days to
   Christmas,
Only three more days of growing wild.
Then a woodman with a chopper
Made me come a cropper
And sold me to some snotty little child.

Now I'm stuck up in a pot beside the window
And all decked out with tinsel and with lights,
But when Christmas is all done
They'll throw me out again,
It's no wonder I have trouble sleeping nights.

Answers

Something Easy to do After your Christmas Dinner! (page 10)

		¹H				²A	
	³S	T	O	C	K	I	N	G
		H				G	
⁴P	A	N	⁵T	O	⁶M	I	M	E
U			U		A		E	
D			R		⁷R	E	⁸D	
⁹D	O	N	K	E	Y		¹⁰E	L	¹¹F
I			E				E		A
N			Y		¹²C	A	R	O	L	L
¹³G	O	O	S	E					L
									S

127

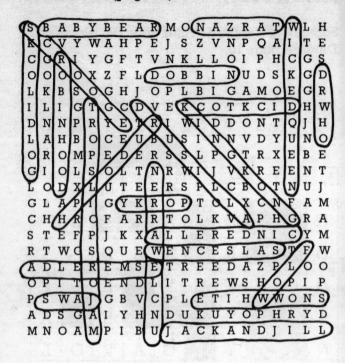

```
S B A B Y B E A R M O N A Z R A T W L H
K C V Y W A H P E J S Z V N P Q A I T E
C O R I Y G F T V N K L L O I P H C G S
O O O O X Z F L D O B B I N U D S K G D
L K B S O G H J O P L B I G A M O E G R
I L I G T G C D V E K C O T K C I D H W
D N P R Y E T R J W I D D O N T Q J H O
L A H B O C E U B U S I N N V D Y U N O
O R O M P E D E R S S L P G T R X E B E
G I O L S O L T N R W I J V K R E E N T
L O D X L U T E E R S P L C B O T N U J
G L A P I G Y K R O P T O L X C N F A M
C H H R O F A R R T O L K V A P H G R A
S T E F P J K X A L L E R E D N I C Y M
R T W C S Q U E W E N C E S L A S T F W
A D L E R E M S E T R E E D A Z P L O O
O P I T O E N D L I T R E W S H O P I P
P S W A J G B V C P L E T I H W W O N S
A D S G A I Y H N D U K U Y O P H R Y D
M N O A M P I B U J A C K A N D J I L L
```